Dealing and Healing with Parkinson's Disease and Other Health Conditions

A WORKBOOK FOR BODY, MIND & SPIRIT

ANGELA & KARL ROBB

PUBLISHED BY ROBBWORKS LLC
FAIRFAX, VIRGINIA

Many thanks to Karen Painter, the designer of the PD Tulip and Jean Burns the illustrator who brought the tulip to life. Visit www.pdtulip.org to learn about the PD tulip.

The information contained in this workbook is intended to provide helpful and informative material on the subjects addressed. It is not intended to serve as a replacement for professional medical, legal, or financial advice. Any use of the advice in this workbook is at the reader's discretion. The author and publisher specifically disclaim any and all liability arising directly or indirectly from the use or application of any information contained in this book. A health-care professional or attorney or financial advisor should be consulted regarding your specific situation. The intent of the author is to offer information of a general nature to help you in your quest for enhanced well-being. In the event you use any of the information in this workbook for yourself, the author and the publisher assume no responsibility for your actions.

Some of the material in this workbook was originally published in the blog http://www.asoftvoice.com.

Publisher: RobbWorks LLC
Email: asoftvoice@robbworks.com
Website: http://www.robbworks.com

Interior and cover design by Gus Yoo
ISBN 978-0-9881847-4-9 (paperback)
ISBN: 978-0-9881847-5-6 (ebook)

1. Health 2. Disease and Physical Ailments 3. Self-Help 4. Parkinson's Disease
5. Alternative Medicine 6. Aging 7. Nervous System 8. Motivational
9. Holistic 10. Workbook

Dedication

To those living with a chronic illness and those people who care about them –
you inspire us each and every day!

It is our hope that this book makes a significant and positive impact on your
health and life.

Table of Contents

Appendix

Acknowledgements

Thank you to our friends, family, and loyal supporters for all of your friendship and goodwill. Our hearts go out to our many mentors and teachers who helped to guide us on our path.

This workbook began as a vision and now is a reality. What was once a dream is here! This workbook transcends the sole condition of Parkinson's disease and has been modified to assist anyone facing a health condition.

Sincere thanks to Jean Strohl for her editing prowess, Sonia Gow for her valuable input, and Gilbert Gallego for his writing contribution.

Angela and Karl Robb
2016

Photograph by Erick Gibson, www.erickgibson.com

From The Authors

In 2012, we published our first book, *A Soft Voice in a Noisy World - A Guide to Dealing and Healing with Parkinson's Disease.* We were pleasantly shocked at the immediate success of the book and are grateful to have touched so many lives - our goal was to help just one life.

The focus of our first book was mostly for those living with Parkinson's disease, but our readers reported to us that our advice and suggestions for Parkinson's transcended beyond just this one illness. We took their suggestions and wrote this workbook for anyone facing any health or life condition.

Here it is, an all-inclusive workbook for those people who are looking for a different outlook. We hope you find something unique and helpful here!

It is our wish that this workbook stimulates thoughts and produces hours of insightful contemplation and healthy discussion. If you choose to use this workbook without having access to either the paperback or the audio book of *A Soft Voice in a Noisy World,* you may not have full understanding of the authors' experience—but we do think you will still find it to be worthwhile and enlightening.

It is our hope that you are challenged by some of the questions that we pose. Best of luck on your journey.

Angela and Karl

How to Use This Workbook

The exercises in this workbook are designed to expand your mind, renew your spirit, and add to your toolkit for greater dealing and healing. This workbook is designed for anyone facing a health or life condition. Whether you are newly diagnosed or living with a health condition for a number of years, this workbook is a tool that can benefit both *individuals* and *groups*. These exercises can also be used by carepartners/caregivers, family members, friends, social workers, therapists or any type of health care professional who works with someone facing illness.

How do I/we use this workbook?

➢ Each chapter of this workbook will include a series of questions, suggestions for discussion, and potential exercises that are helpful in expanding your thoughts and feelings of where you are, at the time.

➢ We suggest that you ponder these questions to truthfully assess and monitor how you are doing.

➢ Go at your own pace.

➢ You may want to make notes in the workbook, in a journal, on a piece of paper, typing or speaking your answers into your phone, tablet, or a computer using voice to text software.

➢ Over time, you may want to revisit questions and previous answers.

➢ You may receive even greater benefit using *A Soft Voice in a Noisy World* with this workbook, however this is **NOT** mandatory.

How you use this workbook is up to you!

FAQs

What does *dealing and healing* mean?

➢ From the authors' perspective: Dealing means that we are *taking action* and working through our health concerns. Healing means that we are *doing our best* to get better every day!

What does the phrase *my health condition* mean?

➢ As mentioned in the *From the Authors* section, a large number of readers of *A Soft Voice in a Noisy World* (our first book), did not have Parkinson's disease, found that the book applied to life in general and not only living with Parkinson's. To accommodate readers seeking perspective on health and life conditions, we added this phrase.

Why should I/we use this workbook?

➢ To find inspiration/motivation.

➢ To initiate new ideas.

➢ To generate conversation.

➢ To hone awareness.

➢ To provide groups with new topics.

➢ To offer facilitators some fresh discussion starters.

➢ To expand perception of dealing with overall health and wellness.

➢ To lead you to your place of dealing and healing.

Who should use this workbook?

➣ Everyone who is:

  ○ Inquisitive

  ○ Explorative

  ○ Imaginative

What do the symbols within the chapters mean?

(i) Do You Know? – Means informational content to dig deeper into a chapter or idea.

(i) Do You Know?
Section Names and Chapter Titles

CHAPTER X
REFER TO PAGE XX IN *ASV*

The chapter titles and sections in this book are either identical titles or slightly updated chapter titles from the *A Soft Voice (ASV)* book. The format was done to make it easier for the reader to use the *ASV* book as a guide, if so desired. Suggested exercise instructions for groups and individuals are included within each chapter. There are no strict instructions. These are just suggestions, on each chapter page in order to facilitate either a verbal or written discussion.

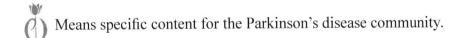 Means specific content for the Parkinson's disease community.

(SG) Exercise instructions are meant for the group leader/facilitator.

Balloon – Additional content or information to pay close attention to...see below.

 Person with Young Onset Parkinson's, Karen Painter, decided that Parkinson's disease needed an internationally recognized symbol. So, she doodled the initial design on a napkin. Her friend and fellow person with Parkinson's Jean Burns illustrated the final digital design and brought the PD tulip to life. Visit www.pdtulip.org to learn about the PD tulip.

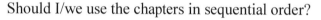

Should I/we use the chapters in sequential order?

➤ It is up to the individual or support group facilitator on how best to use the workbook to fit your needs. You may also consider choosing a chapter by topic.

How should I/we record my responses?

➤ You may want to make notes in the workbook, in a journal, on a piece of paper, typing or speaking your answers into your phone, tablet, or computer using voice to text software.

➤ You may want to discuss questions and your answers with your carepartner/ caregiver, family, friends, social worker, doctor, or health care professionals.

Where should I/we use this workbook?

➤ These exercises can be used anytime, anywhere. You may find them helpful in the following situations:

◕ In speaking with your doctor about your health care.

◕ When speaking to your caregiver/family members about your health/life condition.

◕ Bringing up issues within your support group.

Once again, these exercises are not a replacement for medical advice.

For Group Leaders and Facilitators

This workbook is intended to assist support, communication, and discussion groups as well as individuals. This workbook will provide you with suggested questions to *initiate ideas* and *generate conversation* about what is going on in the lives of the group members.

➢ Here are some recommended uses that you may want to consider:

- ❍ If you are using this in a **support group** setting, we recommend that the group leader *pose questions* to the entire group to *stimulate discussion*. The exercises can also be excellent *starters for conversation.*

- ❍ You might want to ask for the group to think more about these and other related topics that come up, *as homework.*

- ❍ You may want to ask participants to either answer the questions either *written or orally.* Ask participants to journal their answers before or after a meeting.

- ❍ You may want to copy or print the exercises to provide handouts for participants.

- ❍ You may also want to *revisit* questions and previous answers, over time.

➢ For a better understanding of the author's perspective, the group could read *A Soft Voice in a Noisy World* (ASV) prior to the group meeting but this is **<u>NOT</u>** required to complete the exercises.

➢ If group members choose to purchase *A Soft Voice in a Noisy World* and use with this workbook, they may receive an even greater benefit, however this is **NOT** mandatory.

   ○ If your **communications group** has both *A Soft Voice in a Noisy World* (ASV) and this workbook – try using both as *reading tools* and have each member *read aloud* by assigning selected parts of a chapter.

How you use this companion workbook is up to you, or how your group members decide!

Once again, these exercises are NOT a replacement for medical advice.

You may want to read this pledge before the group, all together or share the reading.

The Pledge of the Ill

REFER TO PAGE 7 IN *ASV*

I accept my illness, but it does not define me. I am so much more, even if my illness masks or prohibits others from seeing who I am. Though I am different, I reserve the right to receive patience, respect, and some level of understanding from those I encounter in my everyday life.

I acknowledge that I have a duty to myself to explore all potential modes of healing whether they are conventional or out of the mainstream. I am worthy of being cared for by medical practitioners who treat me with respect and are willing to listen to me. I deserve to be recognized by my physician or other healthcare provider as a person with a life, not just as someone with a medical problem and a chart. My physician owes me the understanding to speak with me as an equal and as a human being, making my way through life as best as I possibly can.

I am willing to make changes, adjustments, and even sacrifices of monumental proportion if these therapies will assist in my betterment and the betterment of the lives of those around me. I am a representative of all those others, before and yet to follow me, who are afflicted with my very same illness. I will do all that I can for myself and those who are similarly afflicted.

I am on a journey to health and healing. I will share my insights and take time to educate all who will listen to me about my disease. The world needs more compassion, and only through education and understanding can we gain true compassion. I don't need, want, or desire any kind of sympathy, because sympathy is far too close to pity. All I ask for is assistance in moving along my path to achieve, learn, teach, grow, and inspire.

(SG) **If you are a support group leader or facilitator, you may want to go line by line in _The Pledge of the Ill_ and address each statement.**

We encourage you to each write your own pledge. It's your choice: You may choose to share and discuss your new pledges with the group or family/friends.

_____

_____

_____

_____

_____

_____

_____

_____

_____

_____

_____

_____

_____

_____

_____

➢ Do you agree with the Pledge of the Ill?

  ○ What don't you agree with?

PART ONE

If Doctors Had All the Answers, Medicine Wouldn't Be Called a "Practice"

Prelude to a Diagnosis

Answer the following questions to explore your opinions about the challenges of living with a diagnosis.

SG **These questions may be a good discussion starter for those who are newly diagnosed.**

"No man is a good doctor who has never been sick himself."—Chinese proverb

➤ Discuss the above quote.

➤ How can you expect your doctor to understand your situation without walking in your shoes?

"If you're wondering now why I had felt compelled to do Outward Bound, remember that there was a point to doing the program. Even though I was consistently wet, tired, hungry, sore, blistered, bug bitten, and frustrated with my body, I felt a strong connection with Nature. It felt right. It felt powerful. I had set out to complete a challenge. I was doing it to boost my confidence and prove my resilience just like everyone else who does it. Sadly, the outcome had temporarily backfired. Now I was worried about my well-being. No one could give me a real solution to what was happening with my body. I was getting concerned and needed answers." (A Soft Voice in a Noisy World, pg. 21)

The author experienced numerous challenges on his Outward Bound experience, prior to being diagnosed with Parkinson's.

➤ Describe and discuss the challenges that you have faced and overcome, with your health condition.

➤ What has been your biggest challenge with Parkinson's/your health condition?

The Diagnosis

If you are an individual using this workbook: in this next exercise, list your answers to the following questions. You may want to write your answers to these questions on a photocopied version to use and reuse.

(SG) This exercise may be best in a group discussion and harder for a newly diagnosed person. You may want to come back to this question at a later date.

We seem to take time for our doctors but neglect the time we need to take care of ourselves. Dedicate the time you need for yourself. Your doctor can't do it all in 4 to 6 brief visits a year. The time between visits is an opportunity to try new options.

"Drugs are not always necessary. But belief in recovery always is." —Norman Cousins

➢ Any comments on the quote?

Your choice of doctor can be crucial to your health!

Here are Some Questions to Ponder and Discuss:

➢ How long have you been diagnosed?

➢ What was your first notable symptom?

➢ How were you diagnosed?
   ○ Do you think you've had Parkinson's/your health condition longer?

➢ How did you cope mentally prior to your diagnosis?

➢ How did your coping change after your diagnosis?

➤ Have you been able to accept the diagnosis?

➤ Do you ever deny having your health condition? If so, why?

(SG) You may want to try these questions at a time when the group feels comfortable sharing. Some questions may be put aside for another time. Pace yourself.

➤ Do you feel isolated, misunderstood, or alone?

   ○ If so, how?

   ○ What changes can you make to help alleviate these feelings?

➤ Do you have a positive attitude?

   ○ Does the rest of the group agree with your positivity?

   ○ Do you see being positive as a choice?

Frustrations with Doctors

This is a compare and contrast discussion that will help distinguish some important factors that are unique to each person. Don't rush through this exercise.

 You might spend two or more discussions on this one exercise.

Some live their lives on Standard Time.
Others follow Greenwich Mean Time.
The free and easy follow Island Time.
But the unpredictable prescribe to PD Time.

Never knowing, Will my meds work?
Will my body do as I ask of it?
Must I wait and postpone my plans?
PD Time dominates my life and the life of my care partner.

As it is impossible to fit a square peg in a round hole, doctors often fail to recognize the unique situation of each person. Each one of us is unique.

Talk about how different and alike you are to others living with your health condition.

➢   Backgrounds

➢   Ages

➢   Medication Regimen

   ○ Medication side effects

➢   Symptoms

➢   Physical Challenges

➢   Cognitive Challenges

➢   Beneficial Activities

➤ Exercise

➤ Complementary Therapies

⊚SG Spend 5 to 10 minutes discussing how Parkinson's/your health condition affects each of us.

➤ Why are we all so different, yet we all supposedly have the same disease?

➤ Is Parkinson's/my health condition one disease?

Finding the Right New Doctor

Consider the following questions to explore what it is you want or need in a new physician.

➣ Are you satisfied with your neurologist? General practitioner? Cardiologist? Dermatologist? Etc.?

  ◯ Why or Why not?

➣ What traits do you want in your neurologist? Other doctors?

➣ What do you want your general practitioner to know or understand about Parkinson's/your health condition?

  ◯ What can you do to assist with their understanding?

 What is a Movement Disorder Specialist?

As defined by the American Academy of Neurology® (www.aan.com):
  Movement disorder specialists are neurologists who have studied an additional one to three years in a movement disorder program, or specialize in treating people with Parkinson's disease and other movement disorders.

Do you see a Movement Disorder Specialist?

  ◯ If not, do you know if there is a Movement Disorder Specialist in your area?

Is Your Current Doctor Satisfactory?

Ask the following questions to determine your satisfaction with your current doctor(s).

A good fighter needs a good team behind him or her.

Make sure your doctor listens to you and sticks to your plan.

Are You Happy with Your Doctor?

- Is your doctor up to speed on new developments in your field of need? Y/N
- Does your doctor return your phone calls on a timely basis? Y/N
- Is your doctor usually on time? Y/N
- Is the doctor's office accommodating in helping you get your medications and refills when you need them? Y/N
- Does your doctor seem to care about your condition? Y/N
- Does your doctor have an open mind about complementary therapies? Y/N
- How is your doctor's bedside manner? Satisfactory/Unsatisfactory

CHAPTER 5

➢ Does your doctor listen to you and do you feel you have good communication with him/her?

➢ Have you researched your doctors?

➢ Do you and your doctor work well together? Is there a plan?

➢ Does your carepartner/caregiver/family member participate in your appointments?
   ○ Have you shared your care plan with your spouse/caregiver/family?

Getting a Second Opinion

Discuss comfort levels and what it would take to make you consider getting a second opinion or replacing your current doctor. Loyalty is admirable, but it can have consequences.

When it involves your health, seek peace of mind.

➤ Discuss the above quote.

➤ Have you had doctors who refuse to listen to you?

  ❍ If so, how did you cope with the situation?

  ❍ What action did you take?

Share your knowledge and learn from others!

Doctors are Human

Use the following questions to discuss what a care team is and how it can be helpful to you.

 This is a great sharing exercise for group members.

We place a great deal of trust in our doctors. While most doctors are quite capable, the act of improving our wellness depends on what we do between doctor visits.

 Do You Know?

What is a Care Team?

A patient care team is a group of diverse clinicians who communicate with each other regularly about the care of a defined group of patients and participate in that care.

Source: Starfield B. Primary care: concept, evaluation, and policy. New York: Oxford University Press; 1992

In *A Soft Voice,* Karl describes his trials and tribulations with the doctors on his care team. It is important for the person with a health condition to be informed about management, medications, and the latest research. This knowledge will come in handy to help make informed decisions and be respected as part of your care team.

➤ Who is on your care team?

   ○ What disciplines/healthcare specialists are on your care team?

➤ What are you doing to improve your knowledge of your health condition?

➤ How can you facilitate better communication between your doctors?

☞ See next page for Creating Your Care Team Action Plan.

CHAPTER 7

Creating My Care Team Action Plan

I have a good (+) or I need a (?):

☐ Physician   ☐ Physical Therapist

☐ Neurologist   ☐ Occupational Therapist

☐ Dentist   ☐ Speech Therapist

☐ Physical Trainer   ☐ Nutritionist

☐ Massage Therapist   ☐ Eye Doctor

☐ Yoga Instructor   ☐ Other

☐ _____   ☐ _____

☐ _____   ☐ _____

If I need:

A ride – I can call _____

Food delivery – I can call _____

My doctor – I can call _____

A health advocate – I can call _____

A friend to talk to – I can call _____

Keep Good Records and Remind Your Doctors

Read the following excerpt from *A Soft Voice* **and answer the questions concerning record keeping for your health condition.**

 **You may want your communication group members to practice their skills to read the excerpt out loud.**

Vigilance and good record keeping is very important with a health condition.

➤ Do you keep good records?

○ Do you keep a list of your medical procedures?

➤ Do you understand your medications?

○ Do you know why you are taking them?

○ Are you aware of potential side effects?

○ Do you carry a list of your medications with you, in case of emergency?

○ Do you document any side effects that you recognize from your medications and share them with your physician?

➤ Do you know your medication schedule?

○ Do you follow it?

○ Do you carry your medication schedule with you, in case of emergency?

Understanding your medications, medication schedule, and side effects is important, particularly when a change is made in your medication regimen.

Here are a few useful tips direct from *A Soft Voice:*

➡ Keep good records of your medications. If one doctor adds a new drug to your regimen, be in charge of notifying the other doctors you see, so they can update their files.

➡ Track your responses to your treatment. Make note of any symptoms or changes in your condition that you experience. Your doctor may be of help to you to distinguish between side effects of taking meds and signs of the progression of Parkinson's/my health condition.

➡ Read the package inserts that come with your medications and make note of possible side effects. Talk with your pharmacist if you have questions.

➡ Read about drugs, treatments, and tests on reputable medical and patient advocacy sites on the Internet; however, be cautious about believing everything you read. Information found online has not necessarily been reviewed and could be wildly inaccurate. Read with an eye toward knowing what kinds of questions to ask your doctor and to be informed of possible alarm signals.

➡ Have your pharmacist check the database for possible adverse drug interactions.

➡ Create a portable binder of your medical history, which includes contact names, phone numbers, emails, and street addresses of every doctor and institution that has treated or tested you, as well as your up-to-date insurance information.

➡ Take notes or use a voice recorder at your appointment.

➡ When you have a new test done and receive results, be sure to send a copy to each of your doctors for whom this is appropriate (examples, neurologist, general practitioner, internist, and cardiologist), and so on.

☞ Turn to the next page for Health and Travel document!

Ask Your Doctor for a "Health and Travel Document"

A travel letter can be a helpful tool to introduce yourself as someone with a health condition to Transportation Security Administration (TSA) or other federal or international authorities.

RE: John Doe, Patient #1234

To Whom It May Concern:

Mr. John Doe, the bearer of this letter, is my patient and under my care and treatment. He is afflicted with early onset of Parkinson's disease. This illness may cause him to move awkwardly or erratically. Unless Mr. Doe tells you otherwise, there should be no reason for concern about his movement. The medications that he is taking can cause uncontrollable flailing or shaking, but it will wear off.

Parkinson's patients can display numerous symptoms such as: balance issues, gait problems, stumbling, and uncontrollable running to maintain balance, slurred or stuttered speech, stiffness, tremor, falling, and hunched posture. At times, please be aware that Mr. Doe is susceptible to these symptoms and actions.

Mr. Doe's condition is not a threat to anyone. Please be patient, understanding, and considerate. Parkinson's patients show more symptoms when rushed, stressed, and put under pressure. Thank you.

Sincerely,
[Signature]
Doctor's Name, M.D.

➢ Do you have a travel letter?

    ❍ If not, would you consider having one while travelling?

    ❍ What steps can you take to ensure your travel is smooth?

Chapter 24 includes additional travel tips and questions.

How to Talk to Doctors

It is important to build a rapport and establish a presence with your doctor. Being on time, prepared and ready to be an active part of your healthcare team is a huge leap to showing your involvement and lays great groundwork for getting your doctor's attention and respect.

Having a list of concerns or questions ready to go, will move the appointment along and show the doctor what needs addressing. This is in addition to any forms your doctor may have you complete online or at the office, before your appointment. It is best to complete these forms at home prior to your visit, especially if you have difficulty with your handwriting.

☞ <u>See the next page</u> for a form that could be used as a starting point for your appointments – use for your doctor and/or for yourself. It may be beneficial to you and your doctors to fill these out on a regular basis and take them to your next appointment.

CHAPTER 9

Notes for My Doctor's Appointment

Name:
Date:
Reason for visit:

Most days, I feel _____

I would like to work on _____

My spouse/loved one/carepartner/family member says _____
_____

For those with Parkinson's: Biggest "off time?" _____

Any new symptoms or side effects? _____
_____

My chief complaint is_____

What has changed since my last appointment is _____
_____

What has gotten better since my last appointment is _____
_____

I need help with _____
_____

I need these prescription refills _____
_____
_____
_____

What new research or medications should I know about?

How might these help me?

What should I also consider using?

Timeline Exercise

Complete this form and discuss with your doctor. Place a dot on the timeline when you: take medications, eat, exercise, have symptoms (tremor for example) or side effects (dyskinesia for example). Use a different color for each separate activity or different medication.

If you do share your timeline, add a color coded legend:

○ Medications

○ Eating

○ Exercise

○ Symptoms (describe here)

○ Side Effects (describe here)

6AM	7AM	8AM	9AM	10AM	11AM	12PM	1PM	2PM	3PM	4PM	5PM

6PM	7PM	8PM	9PM	10PM	11PM	12AM	1AM	2AM	3AM	4AM	5AM

PART TWO

Living with Parkinson's Disease or Other Health Conditions

Coping with a Diagnosis

The following questions take a closer look into coping with a diagnosis. Answer as honestly as you can.

(SG) **Encourage group members to participate and share their answers. Be respectful if they choose not to share.**

There is no right way or wrong way to cope with your diagnosis. It is our belief that one is not capable of starting the healing process as long as they remain in denial.

How Do You Deal with Change?
Answer these questions about change - you might discover something new about yourself!

➢ How are you at accepting change?

➢ How do you accept, cope, and move on?

"It all depends on how we look at things, and not on how they are in themselves."
—Carl Jung

➢ Talk about this quote.

"Change the way you look at things and the things you look at change."
—Dr. Wayne Dyer

➢ Do you believe that your perspective can make a difference in how you react or behave? If so, how?

➢ Do you think that maybe if you change how you look at your illness, you might be able to work better with it?

➢ Have you told your employer, family members, kids, and friends about your diagnosis?

○ Why? Why not?

CHAPTER 10

Martin E.P. Saling, Ph. D said in his book, *Learned Optimism:*

"Life inflicts the same setbacks and tragedies on the optimist as on the pessimist, but the optimist weathers them better."

➢ What is your reaction to the above quote?

Keeping secrets can add to stress and make symptoms worse. Consider sharing your diagnosis with someone you trust.

My Health Condition Doesn't Mean the End

Use the following questions to discuss your emotional and mental outlook toward your health condition.

Your illness may mean a transition - not the end.

"Hope is the thing with feathers that perches in the soul—and sings the tune without the words—and never stops—at all."—Emily Dickinson No. 254

➢ What has your health condition taught you?

➢ Do you appreciate what you have and show gratitude for the good in your life?

➢ Has your health condition made you more aware of your other senses?

➢ Has it made you more sensitive? More aware?

➢ What adjustments are you considering to live well with your diagnosis?

Prior to living with a health condition, multi-tasking may have been easy. Living with a health condition can make it harder to keep focus. It is easy to allow our minds to lose focus and wander. If we lose sight of the present, we tend to miss details.

➢ How are you at living in the present?

➢ What do you do to keep yourself centered and balanced?

➢ Does your mind wander?

➢ Can you stay on task?

➢ Do you prioritize well?

➣ Do you start projects but don't finish them?

➣ How is your attention span?

If your answers indicate you need a little help in staying centered and balanced, we strongly suggest that you seek out yoga, meditation, and other practices in your area for centering mind and body!

 Do You Know?

Cognitive Changes and Parkinson's

According to the Parkinson's Disease Foundation (www.pdf.org) website, in an article titled: _Not Just a Movement Disorder: Cognitive Changes in PD_, Dr. Laura Marsh discusses some of the non-motor symptoms of Parkinson's that could affect those living with Parkinson's.

> _"PD affects a variety of cognitive functions. Problems with executive function are often regarded as the most common. Executive functions are higher-order mental processes such as problem-solving and planning, initiating and following through on tasks, and multi-tasking ideas or projects."_

If you think that you or your loved one with Parkinson's is having difficulties with these issues, we recommend you bring them to the attention of your care team: movement disorder specialist, neurologist or general practitioner for discussion.

Source: Parkinson's Disease Foundation -http://www.pdf.org/en/winter07_08_Not_Just_a_Movement

This Disease Isn't Fair

Be honest with yourself as you fill in these blanks:

1. I am willing to _____ for my health condition.

2. My health condition has limited my ability to: _____
   _____

3. My health condition has given me _____
   _____

4. The one thing I would like to understand about my health condition is
   _____

5. I am exploring and looking into _____
   _____ for my health condition.

6. I consider myself to be a/an _____ when I get
   up in the morning.

7. When I go to bed, my philosophy is _____

8. I think you should know this about me: _____

9. My health condition has taught me _____
   _____

10. What can I do for _____?

If you want a more in-depth pursuit of these exercises, see the Appendix for additional questions.

Depression

 According to the National Parkinson Foundation:

> *It is estimated that at least 50 percent of those diagnosed with PD will experience some form of depression during their illness, and up to 40 percent will experience an anxiety disorder. In fact, new research from NPF's 2012 Parkinson's Outcomes Project found that taken together, mood, depression and anxiety have the greatest impact on health status, even more than the motor impairments commonly associated with the disease.*

> Source: National Parkinson Foundation - http://parkinson.org/understanding-parkinsons/non-motor-symptoms/depression

Depression is real and should never be discounted! **We are NOT experts on this important subject,** but we do know it can turn a life upside down, if not treated properly with a medical team, medication, therapy, diet and exercise. We do believe massage and other touch therapies, like Reiki, can be beneficial. Depression is a very serious part of any health condition and should be treated by a professional!

➤ The National Parkinson Foundation recommends that people with Parkinson's disease:

  ○ Get screened for depression at least once a year.

  ○ Discuss changes in mood with their healthcare professional and doctor.

  ○ Bring a family member to doctor's appointments to discuss changes in their mood.

Most of the national/international Parkinson's disease organizations have depression and anxiety information online. Here are just a few of the resources available:

➤ Parkinson Disease Foundation
http://www.pdf.org/en/depression_pd

➢ National Parkinson Foundation
http://parkinson.org/understanding-parkinsons/non-motor-symptoms/depression

➢ Davis Phinney Foundation – From Every Victory Counts® manual:
http://www.davisphinneyfoundation.org/living-pd/victory-counts/

  ○ Mood and Behavior: Depression worksheet

  http://www.davisphinneyfoundation.org/wp-content/uploads/
  downloads/2014/08/DPF-5.15-depression-worksheet-2014.pdf

  ○ Mood and Behavior: Anxiety worksheet

  http://www.davisphinneyfoundation.org/wp-content/uploads/
  downloads/2014/07/DPF-5.13-anxiety-worksheet-2014.pdf

If you have any questions about depression and Parkinson's disease or your health condition, we encourage you to discuss these issues with your movement disorder specialist, neurologist or healthcare provider as soon as possible!

Be Good to Yourself

These questions are designed to get you to think about yourself and possibly discover something new.

Part of taking care of yourself is to be your best! This may require you to put yourself first, but not at the detriment of your loved ones and those around you. Being good to yourself will make you better for all those around you!

"Make the best use of what is in your power, and take the rest as it happens."—Epictetus

➣ What do you think of the quote above?

➣ What do you enjoy? What brings you pleasure?

➣ How do you have fun?

➣ Are you good to yourself?

○ Are you good to those around you?

➣ Are you more reactionary, realistic, or logical?

➣ How well do you listen to others?

➣ Are you doing your best (diet, rest, attitude, therapies, exercise, etc.)?

○ If not, what changes have you considered or can you implement to take better care of yourself?

We are often harder on ourselves than our worst enemy. Give yourself a break!

Timing in Parkinson's Disease/My Health Condition May Be Everything

Completing the exercises below may provide you a way to communicate better with your healthcare team.

Trying to juggle food, medicines, and time of day can be very difficult to keep on track. Each day is different and a challenge.

Timing medication takes diligence, practice and a dash of luck.

➢ Do you agree with the above statement?

➢ How important do you think timing is in managing your health? Rate your answer on a scale of 1-10 with 1 being low and 10 being high.

Timeline Exercise
Complete this form and discuss with your doctor. Place a dot on the timeline when you: take medications, eat, exercise, have symptoms (tremor for example) or side effects (dyskinesia for example). Use a different color for each separate activity or different medication. Colored pencils or markers could be used.

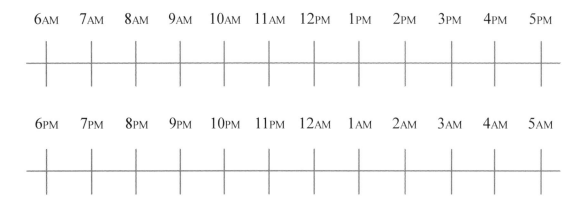

Copy these pages so you can reuse this exercise and share with your health care providers. If you do share your timeline, add a color coded legend:

○ Medications

○ Eating

○ Exercise

○ Symptoms (describe here)

○ Side Effects (describe here)

In Search of Daily Tools
Maintaining balance between mind, body and spirit is essential to managing any health condition. Here are some options you may want to try to add to your toolkit. Make time each day to tend to your body, mind and spirit.

Body Tools – massage, Qigong, Tai Chi, reflexology, acupuncture, acupressure, Feldenkrais, Trager, Reiki.

Mind Tools – meditation, brain exercises.

Spirit Tools – journaling, prayer, meditation, volunteering.

If you have tried or use any of these, consider sharing your experiences with others. As your needs change, always consider other modalities in the future.

Find tools to structure and balance your life.

Structure Your Life to Gain Some Control

The questions below are designed to help you find your own answers about control and it's role in your life.

Talk a bit about what control really is and what it isn't.

Managing Your Daily Life
Factors related to your daily life and routine may play a major role in how well you live and how well you manage your health condition.

Consider these for example or add your own:

Diet	Exercise	Stress
Sleep	Climate	Noise
Anxiety	Fear	Negativity
Rage	Denial	

➤ Which of these factors have most impacted your health condition?

   ○ What are you doing for yourself to counteract the effect(s)?

➤ Do you keep a daily structure or routine?

➢ Have you re-structured your day? Life?

➢ Do you take your medication(s) on time?

Keeping a schedule has benefits! Even a small change can have a huge impact. When making changes, don't make more than one change at a time. Multi-tasking/multi-changes can be difficult to handle and too much for those of us living with a health condition.

➢ What does *"living well"* with a health condition really mean to you?

➢ Quality of life versus quantity of life is something worth talking about whether you have a health condition or not. Which of these is most important to you?

Just like the "butterfly effect"—a small change in your life can have huge outcomes!

Driving

The questions below will not only spur a dialogue with your friends and family but also provide an opportunity for you to have an internal dialogue with yourself on this complex issue.

SG **Make sure to have additional resources for your area available when discussing this issue with the group.**

Excuses can't change fact.

➤ Do you agree with the quote?

➤ Have you considered putting up your keys?

○ If so, have you discussed your decision with your spouse, significant other, family and/or friends?

○ Have you had a driving assessment?

➤ When you drive, are you a threat to others, your family or yourself?

○ Have others mentioned their concerns to you?

➤ Is your reaction time sufficient either to brake or to accelerate, fast enough to avoid a potential accident?

➤ Have you had a fender bender or worse in the last few months? Any close calls?

➤ Could you share a ride or get a ride from friends, family or spouse?

➤ Have you researched transportation alternatives in your area (Bus, Metro, Rail, Taxi, Uber/Lyft, ride services, volunteer transportation services, churches)?

Many localities have transportation resources available for those who do not drive. Check with your local Agency on Aging or social services for more information.

ⓘ Do You Know?

Driving Assessments

Check with your local **Division of Motor Vehicles (DMV)** for assessment resources.

National Parkinson Foundation article: Driving with PD
http://www.parkinson.org/understanding-parkinsons/living-well/activities-of-daily-living/driving-with-pd

The **Association for Driver Rehabilitation Specialists (ADRS)** has a resource listing of Certified Driving Rehabilitation Specialists (CDRS) who can provide a driving assessment and also provide driving rehabilitation resources. Visit http://www.aded.net to search the resource directory for someone near you.

Giving up your keys does not mean foregoing your freedom. Do what is best for everyone in your life.

Two-headed Monster

These exercises are an opportunity to creatively express your feelings about your health condition.

(SG) **You may want to provide extra paper, pens, markers, etc. for group members who want to expand on this exercise. Also, please remind group members that sharing their art is their decision.**

Draw your vision of what you perceive Parkinson's disease/your health condition to look like.

CHAPTER 18

Yin Yang symbol – According to Wikipedia,"*In Chinese philosophy, yin and yang (also yin-yang or yin yang, 陰陽 yīnyáng "dark—bright") describes how opposite or contrary forces are actually complementary, interconnected, and interdependent in the natural world, and how they give rise to each other as they interrelate to one another.*"

Source: https://en.wikipedia.org/wiki/Yin_and_yang

As much as Parkinson's or any health condition takes, if we look hard at the lessons, there is something to be learned.

➢ Share two things your health condition has taken from you.

➢ Share two things your health condition has given you.

Sickness Happens

Using the questions below delve into your feelings about fear and courage. Share your suggestions on where and how you find courage.

"Courage is being scared to death and saddling up anyway." – John Wayne

➢   What do you think of this quote?

➢   Where and how do you find courage, daily?

➢   What scares you? Create a list of your fears.

➢   How do you deal with fear?

➢   Does fear hold you back?

➢   What do you need to do to move forward?

Discuss overcoming fears with the group and/or your support system.

<u>You</u> are in the best position to help yourself.

Ten Tips for Dealing with My Health Condition

Read the list of ten tips below and think about what tips you would add.

(SG) These tips could be read aloud as a voice exercise.

Read and review this list of ten tips from *A Soft Voice*.

10. Look deep inside yourself and face your disease head on. Understanding its symptoms and possible treatments for it would be a good start.

9. Seek inspiration around you. There is courage, strength, and beauty all around us in children, animals, nature, scenery, books, music, film, art, and spirit.

8. Identify a hero or role model; be inspired by someone you look up to. Get invigorated by someone who overcame adversity. This will strengthen your survival instinct. People are doing amazing feats and overcoming huge obstacles. You can, too!

7. Build a network of family and friends. Create a community of people that energizes you. Find or develop a support group, or at least participate in an online chat room for people with Parkinson's or your specific condition.

6. Get involved in efforts to fund research, create awareness, and attend lectures and symposiums for your condition. Your actions can lead to change. Share your story.

5. Consider going vegetarian - for better health and for a better planet.

4. Continue to dream and don't lose hope. What inspires you? Pursue it!

3. Be open and willing to explore new treatment options that may offer relief, but which are not invasive and cannot harm you.

2. Take charge of your life and body. Exercise as best you can.

1. Do what you can, when you can, especially if it brings you joy!

➣   Brainstorm your own tip list and share it with the group.

_____

_____

_____

_____

_____

_____

Think differently! Be open to new ideas and suggestions from others.

Visit www.asoftvoice.com for other lists of tips, and much more!

Voice

Answer the questions below to delve into the issue of voice problems due to health conditions.

We recommend to group leaders that you have voice resources available for your members to discuss as part of this chapter.

Your voice is your connection to the world and your key form of communication. Some health conditions can take away your ability to communicate, but you must do your best, so that you are heard and understood!

➤ Have you had voice problems?

○ Have you tried or considered getting help with your voice?

➤ Do you think you need help with your voice?

➤ How often are you asked to repeat yourself?

➤ Could your voice use improvement?

There are options to help with the voice like the SPEAK OUT!® developed by the Parkinson Voice Project (http://www.parkinsonvoiceproject.org), Lee Silverman Voice Treatments (LSVT LOUD®) and LSVT BIG® (http://www.lsvtglobal.com) developed by LSVT Global, Inc.

Do You Know?

What causes speech and swallowing issues in Parkinson's disease?

Speaking and swallowing are highly-automatic behaviors. When we speak, we don't think about taking air into our lungs, contracting our diaphragm, or moving our vocal folds, tongue or lips—it all happens automatically. It's the same for swallowing—it's an automatic behavior.

Dopamine facilitates automatic movements. However, in Parkinson's, there is a considerable loss of dopamine. With less dopamine, automatic movements are disrupted, which can contribute to speech and swallowing difficulties.

Source: Parkinson Voice Project - http://parkinsonvoiceproject.org/Patients-FAQ.html

Trying to Understand Parkinson's/My Health Condition

Use the questions below to discuss the challenges of educating yourself and others about your health condition.

(SG) Compare and contrast your similarities and differences in the group.

Try walking in someone else's shoes. It isn't always easy to understand, without actually experiencing illness.

➤ Do the people in your life try to understand your Parkinson's disease/your health condition?

➤ What is your biggest challenge in educating others about your health condition?

➤ How do you demystify your health condition?

➤ How do you keep yourself up to date on what's happening in your illness?
- ❍ Websites
- ❍ Webinars
- ❍ Books
- ❍ Newsletters
- ❍ Lectures
- ❍ Conferences
- ❍ Support group
- ❍ Exercise group
- ❍ Communication group
- ❍ Other?

Take Me for a Ride

The questions below deal with the sensitive issue of how others perceive our health condition.

Compassion can lead to understanding of another's challenges.

Some people can be cruel and lack understanding. Sometimes through education, you can teach others. Often, people that you meet may not know how to deal with your health condition.

➤   How would you handle someone who treats you rudely and questions your health condition?

➤   Do you think people are ruder or kinder due to your health condition/challenges?

➤   Do you educate others about your health condition, when you can?

➤   How can you make people aware of your health condition and your needs?

Travel Tips

Discuss the benefits of being prepared for travel.

Stay flexible and retain your sanity.

➤ Do you travel?

  ○ If not, why?

➤ Do you see ways around the obstacles of travel?

  ○ If yes, share some of your tips with the group.

Know Where You Are Going!

It goes without saying that planning in advance for an upcoming trip and making preparations ahead of time can make a trip much less stressful. It's better to make time to prepare, instead of letting stress cause havoc with your health condition! Chapter 8 includes additional travel tips and questions.

➤ Get your caregiver/carepartner involved in your trip planning.

➤ Research airports, train stations, and bus depots online for maps and accessibility before you travel. Knowing the shortest path when you travel can save you some energy!

➤ Call ahead! Let people know you have mobility issues, need special accommodations for your trip including: airline, hotel, rental car, train, bus etc.

➤ Know where the elevators are located.

➤ Locate the handicapped ramps in the arrival and departure lanes.

> ➤ Cruises can be quite accommodating since your room travels with you!

The European Parkinson's Disease Association (EPDA) has a document called *The Parkinson's Passport* you can download and print. Visit their website for this document: http://www.epda.eu.com/en/resources/parkinsons-passport/

Create Your Own Travel Tips

1. _____

2. _____

3. _____

4. _____

5. _____

6. _____

7. _____

8. _____

9. _____

10. _____

My Health Condition Defined

Answer these questions as honestly as you can about what your health condition is to you.

 This exercise can be used as a discussion starter for a group meeting.

The delicate balance of wellness depends on incalculable factors.

Use the space below to write how you define what your health condition is to you. Only you can answer that question. Take a stab at creating an answer in verse, prose, song, dance, or even a single word. Share it with your group or support system:

_____

_____

_____

_____

_____

Writing this down can be helpful in two ways:

1. It lets family and friends know how your health condition affects you and in what ways.

2. It allows for venting of frustrations.

My Health Condition Puts My Life In Focus

In the questions below, the focus is on coping and acceptance. Do your best to express your feelings about these two topics.

(SG) Share your insights with the group or friends/family/others.

Any illness or challenge in our life is a lesson, if we stop to look at it closely!

➢ How are you coping with Parkinson's disease/your health condition?

➢ What coping skills do you need to work on?

➢ Have you lost friends due to your health condition?

➢ Have you made new friends due to your health condition?

This chapter's focus is largely on acceptance.

➢ How are you doing on your level of acceptance?

➢ Are you aware of how some people treat you differently?

➢ How do your friends help you live well with your health condition?

➢ Has your health condition given you a greater appreciation and insight to life?
  ○ If so, how?

It's Only a Matter of Time

Use these exercises to think about schedules in your life. There are additional exercises about time and schedules in Chapters 9 and 15.

Time, both short and long, is not to be wasted.

Distraction and forgetfulness throw schedules off. Try to remain on an hourly routine. Time management and pill management go hand in hand together for optimal benefit.

➤ Is time our friend or enemy?

Time is a huge factor in our lives that can continue to add to our daily grind and increase pressure.

➤ Do you feel pressure to go faster, in general?

➤ Are you good at staying on schedule?

  ○ If not, what changes could you try, to stay on schedule?

➤ Do you live in the here and now? How is your focus?

➤ Are you aware of the impact that stress and pressure play on your health condition?

Is Everything All Right?

Think about your attitude and perspective by answering the questions below.

Don't forget the good things in your life! Every day is special.

➤   How is today special for you?

➤   Is every day special?

Your health condition can bring unwanted attention from either the disease itself or from side effects of the medications.

➤   What strategies do you use to deal with these situations?

➤   Is staying positive difficult for you?

◯ If yes, what tools do you use to shift yourself to a more positive perspective?

◯ If no, what do you do to keep yourself positive?

You are special. Make your life a priority!

Positive Daily Living

Use these exercises to talk about your attitude. You might discover something new about yourself!

Positive is a choice.

"Finish each day and be done with it. You have done what you could. Some blunders and absurdities no doubt crept in; forget them as soon as you can. Tomorrow is a new day; begin it well and serenely and with too high a spirit to be cumbered with your old nonsense."—Ralph Waldo Emerson

➤ How does this quote help you live each day "in the moment"?

➤ Are you an optimist?

➤ Do you find helping others, helps you?

➤ Did any of your teachers/mentors leave a mark or impact on you that has stuck with you?

➤ What do you do to remain upbeat and positive?

Are You an Optimist?

➤ Do you see obstacles as goals and lesson builders?

➤ Do you see the glass as half full or half empty?

➤ Do you worry about things that haven't happened?

➤ Do you focus on the good or the less good?

➤ Are you an optimist? Could you be an optimist?

The Mental Side of Parkinson's/Your Health Condition

Use these questions to ponder how you keep your brain active.

(SG) Ask your group members to share their answers.

Your health condition is a complex illness that affects mind, body, and spirit!

Games, puzzles, and video games can help with your mental and physical dexterity.

➤   What do you do to maintain or improve your cognition?

➤   How do you keep your brain active?

➤   How are you at keeping your mind, body, and spirit in balance?

The Nintendo Wii and PD
Dr. Nathan Ben Herz, OTD, MBA, OTR/L

"In exercise, the production of dopamine has been shown to increase. In some studies, however, exercise has also been shown to improve Parkinson's Symptoms without respect to dopamine the act of performing functional movement goes back to the adage of Use it or lose it- as it relates to Parkinson's disease- and participation in video games has been found to increase dopamine. The Nintendo Wii creates an environment that allows someone to remain active, as well as participate in a safe environment."

Source: Gary D Leith Foundation for Parkinson's Research - http://www.garydleith.org/wii.pdf

Adapting

Use the questions below to think about how living with a health condition requires adapting.

(SG) You may find that these questions may be a starter for an oral discussion.

Transition is a natural process that we need not fight.

➤ Are you able to adapt? Is it difficult for you? Are you flexible?

➤ Give 3 examples of things you can do to reduce stress when making a change.

_____

_____

_____

➤ What changes can you make to weed out the stressors in your life that deter your peace of mind?

When facing a transition, don't change multiple things at once. Handling more than one change at a time can cause confusion and more stress. Be kind to yourself and take things slowly. Ask for help if you need it!

It's a Fast-paced World

Discuss the role of pace and balance in your life.

(SG) **You may find these questions are starters for a deeper discussion about balance in our lives.**

Faster has never proven to be better. Maybe, slowing down has benefits.

"There's more to life than increasing its speed"—Mahatma Gandhi

➤   What do you think of the Gandhi quote?

➤   Do you agree that you can't begin healing if you are in denial?

➤   Do you feel your life is in balance? Do you like the pace?

➤   Do you know what you need to do to put it in balance?
   ○ Do you need help?
   ○ Do you know when to ask for help?

➤   Do you find it to be a challenge to multi-task?

➤   Do you focus more on the past or the future than you do the present?

➤   How do you calm your mind?

PART THREE

Support Groups and Relationships

The Joy of Support Groups

The following questions concern support groups. Be honest with yourself as you answer these questions.

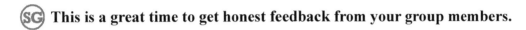 **This is a great time to get honest feedback from your group members.**

If you can't find a support group to fit your needs, consider starting your own. Make your group into what you need for support.

➢   What is your vision of a support group?

➢   In what ways does your support group meet your needs?

➢   Do you see a need for changes?

➢   Are there elements you would like to add or remove?

➢   Do you leave the group feeling empowered? Motivated?

➢   Do you leave feeling educated and better than when you came in?

Try offering new and creative ways to engage and educate the group about your health condition in a way that doesn't drain your energy! For example, you might bring printouts of recent news stories about current research.

ⓘ Do You Know?

There are some additional worksheets in the appendix at the end of this workbook, including suggested support group rules.

Relationships Inside and Out

Coping with change in relationships can be hard. Use these questions to delve into how you feel about this issue.

➤ Do you have a strong support network?

➤ Do you need assistance in building your network?

➤ Is socializing hard for you? If so, why?

    ○ Are you working on building your network?

➤ Have you tried online support websites? Chatrooms? Blogs? Meetings?

➤ Do you feel that the people in your life understand your health condition?

    ○ If not, how do you think it might be better understood?

➤ Do you get judged by a lack of facial expression?

    ○ Has the lack of facial expression caused you communication problems?

      ▪ If so, have you addressed those problems or made your spouse, family, friends, those close to you aware of this issue?

Sometimes stress can cause emotions to erupt. Here are some questions to consider:

➤ On a scale of 1-10, 10 being the highest, what role does stress / anxiety play in your life?

➤ What do you think may be contributing to your emotions?

   ❍ Stress?

   ❍ Diet?

   ❍ Medication?

   ❍ Relationships?

   ❍ Other?

Maintaining Perspective

The questions below are to guide you to reveal your thoughts on empathy for yourself and others.

We are always facing some obstacle, as are our friends, family, and people we care about. Don't let concern for yourself neglect your concern for others. To remain a complete human, we can't lose sight of those near and dear to us. Caring about others keeps us grounded.

➤ Do you feel focused and present to others in your life?

With empathy, we can begin to not put ourselves first at the detriment to those we love. Try to balance your needs and the perspectives of those you care about.

➤ Has it been a challenge for you to care for yourself and to be empathetic about other's needs all at the same time?

➤ If so, what tools have you used to keep your perspective balanced?

To practice empathy:

➤ How can you go about visualizing yourself in another's situation?

➤ Have these questions changed your perspective?

Some Things Don't Change, but People Do

Change plays a large role in our daily lives. Use these questions to explore how you feel about change and labeling.

If you want to change or make changes, it is within your ability.

"What I am looking for is not out there: It's in me." — Helen Keller

➤ Do you agree with the Keller quote and the statement above?

In living with a health condition, things can change without warning. It can be extremely difficult for our loved ones to realize that we have had physical or emotional changes in our condition. We may label these changes. Our loved ones may label these changes. Labeling limits choices and responses. Labeling limits the potential of what could be. Some things just are, and don't need labels. Only by removing labels can we widen our perspective.

➤ Are you quick to label others?

➤ How often do you use the labels 'good' or 'bad'?

➤ What steps can you take to limit your labeling tendencies? For example, how about trying to go through one day without labels?

If you practice going without labels for one day, try going for two days and so on.

Ten Ways to Improve Your Relationships

Read these tips and see if you can add some of your own.

(SG) **This is another exercise communication groups can use to exercise their voices. Encourage your group members to add their tips to this list.**

Patience. Patience. Patience.

Here are a few tips for getting along with the people (and creatures) in your life.

➢ Let go of stupid or insensitive comments, even if someone hurts you.

➢ Tell the people in your life how much they mean to you.

➢ Call a friend you think of often but haven't spoken to for a while.

➢ Do at least one kind deed a day.

➢ Share some helpful knowledge with others.

➢ Give the animals in your life extra time for affection, play, and grooming.

➢ Make the first and last thing you say on a voicemail message be your phone number (and say it slowly and clearly).

➢ The next time you feel angry, try replacing that feeling with compassion for someone else.

➢ A simple smile can brighten your day and another's, too.

➢ Laugh as much as you can. Make someone else laugh, too.

Use this space to create two tips of your own:

_____

_____

_____

_____

_____

_____

_____

_____

_____

_____

_____

_____

_____

_____

_____

_____

_____

_____

_____

_____

_____

Being Touched and Intimacy

Use the following questions to consider the benefits of touch therapies as part of your wellness. Chapter 53 also contains exercises about the importance of touch.

Sharing compassion and touch has healing benefits.

It seems only natural that when a child gets hurt and they are touched with compassion, by their parent(s), healing begins and pain can dwindle.

➢ Do you believe in the power of touch?

    ○ Have you experienced the benefits of touch?

➢ Are you open to trying any touch therapies (massage, reiki, craniosacral, reflexology, etc.)?

    ○ If not, why?

    ○ What is holding you back?

Keeping Relations Alive

Communication is vital part of living well with a health condition and life in general. Use these questions to give communication in your life some attention.

(SG) You may want to broaden these questions even more with additional exercises.

Maintain and nurture friendships and relations.

➢ Do you consider yourself to be an effective communicator?

  ○ If not, what steps can you take to get better?

➢ Are you a good listener?

➢ Do you and your partner communicate?

  ○ If so, how?

➢ Name one way you can communicate better with your partner:

➢ Do you share the good and less good with your partner?

➢ Do you continue to set and try to achieve goals? Even small ones?

What steps do you take to keep your:

➢ Partner relations strong?

_____

_____

_____

_____

➢ Family relations strong?

_____

_____

_____

_____

➢ Friendships strong?

_____

_____

_____

_____

PART FOUR

Reiki, Meditation, and Other Complementary Therapies

Look for Inspiration and Answers

Use the questions below to inspire yourself and reveal new answers.

(SG) **Encourage your group members to participate.**

Don't ever stop seeking answers to questions that have you puzzled!

➤   Are you open to inspiration?

➤   Do you seek meaning? Inspiration? Are you driven?

➤   Who motivates you?

➤   What inspires you?

➤   Do you believe in listening to your gut?

➤   Do you use a mantra?

What is a Mantra?

According to Wikipedia – *Mantra means a sacred utterance, numinous sound, or a syllable, word, phonemes, or group of words believed by some to have psychological and spiritual power in Sanskrit.*

Source: Wikipedia - https://en.wikipedia.org/wiki/Mantra

Mantra from *A Soft Voice*

Give me strength.

Allow me insights to overcome this illness.

I am Strong.
I'll stay Strong.

Phrases That You May Want to Implement in Your Life Exercise

Develop your own mantra. Here are some words and phrases to start you on your way:

I am	I feel	I will overcome
I need	I'm going to	Try
I will	Hopeful	Powerful
Resilient	Endure	I will remain
Full of life	Quest	Change
Curiosity	Empower	Venture
Motivate	Determine	Willing
Pursue	Look for	Hope
Positive	Vigorous	Strong
I love	I choose to live	Give me the strength
Focus on	Power	Strength
Courage	Tenacity	Love

In the space below, create an empowering and powerful phrase that resonates with you and that you can remember throughout the day. See if it brings you strength and confidence.

_____

_____

_____

_____

_____

_____

_____

(i) Do You Know?

What is a Complementary Therapy?

National Center for Complementary and Integrative Health (NCCIH) at the National Institutes of Health (NIH) says:

Many Americans—more than 30 percent of adults and about 12 percent of children—use health care approaches developed outside of mainstream Western, or conventional, medicine. When describing these approaches, people often use "alternative" and "complementary" interchangeably, but the two terms refer to different concepts:

➤ If a non-mainstream practice is used together with conventional medicine, it's considered "complementary."

➤ If a non-mainstream practice is used in place of conventional medicine, it's considered "alternative."

True alternative medicine is uncommon. Most people who use non-mainstream approaches use them along with conventional treatments.

➤ There are many definitions of "integrative" health care, but all involve bringing conventional and complementary approaches together in a coordinated way.

Source: https://nccih.nih.gov/health/integrative-health#cvsa

CHAPTER 40

 In the last fifteen years, there have been some scientific studies of complementary therapies in use for those living with Parkinson's disease.

- *Qigong exercise for the symptoms of Parkinson's disease: a randomized, controlled pilot study. http://www.ncbi.nlm.nih.gov/pubmed/16229022*

- *Tai Chi and Postural Stability in Patients with Parkinson's Disease. http://www.ncbi.nlm.nih.gov/pmc/articles/PMC3285459/*

- *Acupuncture therapy for the symptoms of Parkinson's disease. http://onlinelibrary.wiley.com/doi/10.1002/mds.10134/abstract*

➢ Are you willing to try a complementary therapy?

    ○ If yes, why?

    ○ If not, why?

 If you are looking for a book that discusses Parkinson's disease and the use of complementary therapies, check out Dr. Monique Giroux's book: *Optimal Health with Parkinson's Disease: A Guide to Integrating Lifestyle, Alternative, and Conventional Medicine* by Monique L. Giroux, MD.

Finding Reiki

Use these questions to reflect on your thoughts about Reiki and other complementary therapies.

Find that certain spark that makes a change in your life.

 Do You Know?

What is Reiki?

Reiki is the transferring of the universal energy that is all around us to renew the depletion of our energy. This complementary therapy or modality is available to anyone. Learn more about Reiki at www.givereiki.com.

➢ What do you know about Reiki?

  ○ Would you consider trying Reiki?

  ○ Why or why not?

➢ Have you experienced Reiki?

➢ Do you believe in destiny? Fate? Chance?

➢ Is there a place in your life for Eastern and Western medicine/approaches to work together?

➢ How open are you? 1 (not very open) – 10 (very open)

➢ What have you tried that took you out of your comfort zone?

➢ At first, we were skeptics. Are you a skeptic?

➢ Are you concerned about others' opinions regarding your health choices?

Stress: How We Can Help Ourselves

A heartfelt thank you to Reiki Master Teacher, Gilbert A. Gallego, M.H.R.D. for providing the article for this chapter in the *A Soft Voice* book.

Stress is an important issue in everyone's life. Answer these questions honestly to discover your true feelings on stress and its impact on your health condition.

Stress can come from the unlikeliest of places. As we block and eliminate the stressors, we tend to get better!

➢   What does stress do to you?

➢   Do you know what your stress triggers are?

Here are some examples – feel free to add your own:

Noise	Light	Electricity
Fear and Anxiety	Negativity	Being rushed
Anger	Pain	Being laughed at/stared at
Lack of sleep	Diet	Pressure
Deadlines	Crowds	Impatient people

➢   What tools do you have for dealing with stress?

CHAPTER 42

(i) Do You Know?

What is Self Care?

Self-care is what people do for themselves to establish and maintain health, prevent and deal with illness.

Source: World Health Organization - http://apps.who.int/medicinedocs/en/d/Jwhozip32e/3.1.html

➢ What do you consider self-care?

_____

_____

_____

_____

Meditation Exercise

Either seated in a comfortable chair or lying down - take one minute to focus on an object, the sound of your breath, or heartbeat, and just stay focused for that time. As you gain comfort, try meditating for two minutes Continue to add a minute each time until you reach 5-10 minutes per meditation session or a time you find comfortable.

You may want to consider a meditation app like Headspace (www.headspace.com) to assist your meditation. Meditation takes time and the more you practice, the more refined your practice will become. Stick with it!

Considering Deep Brain Stimulation (DBS)

These questions are specifically designed for those with Parkinson's disease who are considering Deep Brain Stimulation (DBS). These questions are <u>NOT</u> a replacement for medical advice.

This chapter is specifically for those with Parkinson's disease. Some questions may apply to anyone considering surgeries for their health condition.

Know and understand the potential benefits and risks that come with brain surgery or any surgery. Be sure to do your research on the procedure, expected outcome, risks, rehabilitation time, costs, and programming.

Making Decisions:

➢ List the symptoms you hope to improve:

_____

_____

_____

➢ Do you understand the risks, process, and procedure?

➢ Have all your questions been answered sufficiently by your doctor?

➢ Have you spoken to at least 3 people who have received DBS and discussed their experiences?

    ❍ Was their outcome what they had hoped for?

    ❍ Would they do it again?

➢ Have you discussed your decision with your partner/spouse, family, and friends?

Items to Consider:

Programming	Risks of surgeries	Medication may still be required
Disease still progresses	Possible side effects	Costs
Time commitment	Travel	Additional surgeries/battery replacement

ⓘ Do You Know?

There are many books written about Deep Brain Stimulation (DBS) in the Parkinson's disease community. Some of these books are written by people with Parkinson's and some are written by medical professionals. Here's a short listing of those that are currently available by Amazon™.

Books Written by People with Parkinson's and DBS

○ *Life With a Battery-Operated Brain - A Patient's Guide to Deep Brain Stimulation Surgery for Parkinson's Disease* by Jackie Christensen

Books Written by Experts in Parkinson's and DBS

○ *DBS: A Patient Guide to Deep Brain Stimulation* by Sierra M. Farris PA-C & Monique L. Giroux MD

○ *Deep Brain Stimulation: A New Life for People with Parkinson's, Dystonia, and Essential Tremor* by Kelvin L. Chou MD, Susan Grube RN MSN, Parag Patil MD PhD

○ *10 Breakthrough Therapies for Parkinson's Disease* by Michael S Okun MD

The Mind-Body Healing Connection

Use these questions to delve into your thoughts about mind, body, and spirit connections.

When the mind, body, and spirit are all working in harmony, we are whole. If one of those three pieces is out of balance, the others may be affected.

➤ Have you noticed how the mind, body, and spirit are all connected?

➤ Have you explored your own mind/body/spirit connections?

➤ What techniques do you use to keep these three in balance?

➤ What do you do to deal with the stressors (pressure, anxiety, toxins of daily living) in your life?

➤ Do you get angry easily? Sad?

➤ Do you think you have a choice in how you react?

Mind/Body/Spirit Balance Exercises
Complete these statements to get in touch with your inner voice.

Mind Exercise

My mind needs _____

My mind wants _____

My mind can improve from _____

Today, my mind feels _____

I sense _____

My mind says _____

Body Exercise

Today, my body feels _____

My body needs _____

My body wants _____

My body can improve from _____

I sense _____

My body says _____

Spirit Exercise

Today, my spirit feels _____

My spirit needs _____

My spirit wants _____

My spirit can improve from _____

I sense _____

My spirit says _____

A Simple Healing Visualization

Read the visualization below and answer the questions.

This is a simple but powerful tool that you might try for calming the body and helping with mental focus.

Sit in a comfortable spot where you are able to be quiet and calm, such as a comfortable chair or a pillow on the floor. Once you are settled, close your eyes and take a few deep cleansing breaths, and then begin.

At your own pace, calmly take six to twelve calming breaths. On each full breath, slowly inhale through your nose and then exhale through your mouth. Pull air deep into your lungs before you release it. As you expel the air, feel the stress and tension release from any part of your body that carries pain or stiffness. Put any stresses of the day behind you as best you can during these first six to twelve breaths.

With your eyes still closed, envision a small round golden bead. Pure and golden, the bead shines a healing golden light. The bead reminds you of a shiny pearl, but its amber brilliance radiates from the core rather than from an external light source. Energy pulsates from within the tiny orb. Watch as the bead goes into your third eye, right between your eyebrows. Watch as the bead radiates a warm glow that permeates your entire body. The bead has healing powers, and it has come to energize you and return you to a state of health and well-being.

As the bead emanates energy through your third eye it is seeking out any imbalances that exist in your body. Envision the bead scanning your system for toxins and invasive material. As the bead identifies any unwanted structures, it eliminates them. The healing glow of the bead replenishes the depleted cells and snaps them back to their complete potency.

Once the bead has replenished your body, it begins to fade. After the body has been scanned entirely, the bead will slowly dissolve. To conclude the visualization, take three more deep cleansing breaths, and then open your eyes, feeling cleansed and refreshed.

➤ How did this make you feel?

➤ What did you feel or sense?

➤ Did you see a benefit?

➤ Do you think you would use this visualization on a regular basis?

A Releasing Mantra and Affirmation

Read the mantra and then create your own in the space provided. Using a mantra can help you to maintain focus!

"You can clutch the past so tightly to your chest that it leaves your arms too full to embrace the present."—Jan Glidewell

➤ Discuss the quote.

➤ What does this quote say to you?

Here is the mantra mentioned in *A Soft Voice*:

As you breathe in your next breath, silently affirm:

"I am open to healing and making life better with every inhalation."

As you breathe out, silently affirm:

"With every exhalation, I release the toxins, anger, hurt, and fear that hold me in this prison of negativity."

Pause for a moment between breaths. As you do, silently affirm:

"My mind is a powerful tool that must influence my body to initiate change."

Use this page to create your own releasing mantra.

_____

_____

_____

_____

_____

_____

_____

_____

_____

_____

_____

_____

_____

_____

_____

_____

_____

_____

A Visualization for Letting Go of the Past

Read the visualization and answer the questions. You could record the visualization and play the recording whenever you need it.

If we slough off the junk that doesn't serve us, we are cleansing our spirit.

Find a quiet, comfortable place to sit where you won't be disturbed. Close your eyes and breathe. When you feel relaxed, begin your visualization. Imagine you are standing in the middle of a beautiful library. The walls are lined with racks and shelves of books, videos, and journals.

These are the moments and events of your life. Walk to the left and go to a far shelf that has a label on it that reads: "Memories to Keep." Take one of the books off of this shelf and open it to a random page. This is a memory that brings back a pleasant time or event in your life. Allow this memory to replay itself. When you're done, place this book back on the shelf.

Walk to the right and go to a far shelf that reads: "Memories to Discard." The books on this shelf are filled with thoughts and feelings that don't serve you. Each title on this shelf makes up your concerns, fears, anger, or distress. Your energy is robbed by these negative thoughts and feelings, so it is time to get rid of them.

Pick up a book from this shelf of negativity. Rather than opening the book, take it to the corner of the room, where you now notice a vent that reads: "Disposal." Toss the book into the slot and allow yourself to appreciate the feeling as you let go of the thoughts and feelings associated with the memory. Systematically, take each individual book off the shelf in this section of the library and toss it into the disposal slot in the wall. Savor the release that you feel as each book or disturbing memory is destroyed and released from you.

Remember that you can stop whenever you want and take a break. You can come back and dispose of more negative memories, thoughts, and feelings any time it seems like it would be useful.

CHAPTER 47

After reading the visualization, answer these questions:

➤   What did you get out of the visualization?

➤   Did you feel a calming effect come over you?

➤   How do you think you could use this visualization in the future?

➤   How and where else might you use this tool?

There Are Such Things as Miracles

Some things are beyond explanation, but try to envision how you might interpret what you conceive as miraculous.

Miracles come in a multitude of degrees and sizes.

➢   Do you think that miracles happen?

➢   Do you find meaning(s) in everyday life?

➢   What do you plan to work on?

   ⭘ Do you have a plan?

See the Insight Worksheets in the Appendix I for more questions! You might discover something new about yourself. ☺

Celebrate Your Life, Not Your Health Condition

Answer these questions from the perspective of who you really are, not from the point of view of your health condition.

"Life itself is your teacher, and you are in a state of constant learning." – Bruce Lee

➢ Discuss the quote.

➢ Is positivity a choice?

Bruce Lee overcame many obstacles in his life to become a legend and make a lasting impact.

➢ Do you think we are all capable of making such an impact?

➢ Are you an optimist?

  ○ If you don't consider yourself an optimist, what would it take for you to adopt a more positive outlook?

➢ Do you feel a change in outlook can impact your daily life?

➢ Are you able to appreciate the simple things in your life?

  ○ What do you appreciate?

If you are comfortable, share a memory/story with others about something you are grateful for and thankful.

Who Says Parkinsonians Can Only Get Worse?

Answer the questions below to ask yourself about your feelings about choice. The following questions apply not only to people with Parkinson's but also to people with other health conditions.

Unrealistic expectations can overshadow your destination.

"If you think a thing is impossible, you'll make it impossible."—Bruce Lee

➢ Discuss this quote.

➢ Do you notice if you are affected by negative influences?

  ○ If so, what strategies do you use to reduce the impact of negativity?

➢ Are you aware of negative influences, energy, noise, and people? Friends? Family? Places?

➢ Are you open-minded?

➢ Do you believe that you can change, if you want to?

You have a choice! From the moment you wake up in the morning, until you go to bed. Choices are everywhere!

➢ Do you know your "comfort zone"?

➢ Are you willing to go outside your 'comfort zone' for something that may help you?

➢ What <u>one</u> change can you make to overcome the fear of trying something new?

   ○ How do you think you will feel, after this change?

 Do You Know?

Apathy and Parkinson's

In 1991, Dr. RS Marin published in the *Journal of Neuropsychiatry and Clinical Neurosciences* that apathy can occur due to brain damage or neuropsychiatric illnesses such as Alzheimer's, Parkinson's, Huntington's, dementia, or even stroke.

According to the Parkinson's Disease Foundation (www.pdf.org), apathy can affect about 40% of those with Parkinson's without cognitive decline and 60% of those with cognitive decline.

Apathy is a **<u>serious condition</u>** and should be discussed with your primary care doctor, neurologist, movement disorder specialist or mental health care provider to find solutions and tools for you.

Source: https://en.wikipedia.org/wiki/Apathy - J Neuropsychiatry Clin Neurosci. 1991 Summer;3(3):243-54
Parkinson's Disease Foundation - http://www.pdf.org/apathy.

Getting Better

Answer the following questions to gauge your feelings on hope and your health.

Feeling better and getting better begins with a mind shift to knowing that you can get better.

Here are a few thoughts for consideration:

1. You need to be okay in your own skin.

2. You must do your part in getting better.

3. Choose positivity!

   ➢ Where do you find hope?

   ➢ Does your doctor give you hope?

   ➢ What does hope do for you?

   ➢ Do you realize the impact that outside forces play on your symptoms?

   ➢ Do you listen to your body? Mind? Spirit?

What Are You Willing to Do to Help Yourself?

When one is trying to navigate an illness, it isn't always easy to realize that we have choices. If you aren't aware of your options, use these questions to do some investigation so, you can make an educated decision.

"Few people are willing to admit that their mind could be responsible for physical problems when it's much easier to place the blame on someone or something else."
—Robert C. Fulford, D.O.

➣ Discuss this quote!

➣ Do you think you can get better?

➣ Do you believe in yourself?

➣ How far are you willing to go to help yourself?

  ❍ Would you change your diet, your job, and/or your residence to get better?

➣ Would you try a complementary therapy that made little sense to you but may have real benefit?

CHAPTER 52

Self-Scan for Mind/Body/Spirit

Consider these questions as needed to delve into your thoughts and feelings for greater insight.

➢ What are you doing on a daily basis for your Parkinson's/health condition?

➢ How is your mood?

➢ Do you experiment with food sensitivities and allergies?

➢ Have you tried any complementary therapies?

➢ How do you handle stress?

➢ How is your sleep?

➢ Are you happy?

  ❍ What makes you happy?

➢ Are you doing all you can for yourself?

The Power of Touch

Some people find touch to be intrusive and invasive. Touch is a necessary human action that fulfills our needs for warmth and sharing. Touch is an act of compassion and caring. Answer the following questions to address your feelings about the power of touch. Chapter 38 includes additional questions about touch therapies.

➤ How do you feel about being touched?

  ○ If you don't like it, ask yourself, why? Sometimes, those who don't like it need it the most!

Touch can have huge benefits, so come to grips with it and try to work through it.

➤ Do you believe that experiencing something provides a better understanding than a verbal explanation? (e.g. explaining a sunset)

You have to *try it* to understand it.

Try it! Exercise – Even more than once!

Close your eyes, put your hands just below your belly button and breathe, for at least one minute.

➤ What did you notice?

➤ Anything different?

➤ Did you notice any difference in your hands or the place you were touching?

If you are a carepartner/caregiver, try just placing your hand on the base of your loved one's spine!

You may find you will want to practice this exercise on a regular basis. Use this exercise **_anytime_** you need it! You may see a calming state come on.

PART FIVE

Raising Awareness and Effecting Change

Raising Public Awareness

The myths and questions below are specifically targeted to the Parkinson's Disease community.

Awareness comes from being seen and heard. Make your voice heard and your story known by getting involved and making a difference.

"You can't stay in your corner of the Forest waiting for others to come to you. You have to go to them sometimes." —A.A. Milne, Winnie the Pooh

➤ Discuss this quote!

Talk About the Myths:

Myth 1: Only the elderly (and Michael J. Fox) get Parkinson's disease.

Fact: Parkinson's can strike at most any age.

Myth 2: There are one million people in the United States living with Parkinson's disease.

Fact: No one, in the United States, has done a census of how many people have Parkinson's disease.

Myth 3: Having Deep Brain Stimulation (DBS) means that the recipient no longer needs to take medication and the illness is halted.

Fact: While DBS has shown promise and helped many, the patient, often remains on a medication regimen.

Myth 4: People move uncontrollably and rapidly, or experience dyskinesia, as a symptom of their Parkinson's disease.

Fact: Usually, dyskinesias occur when too much medicine is in the patient's system.

Advocacy Can Lead to Change

Telling your personal story is a powerful way to advocate and educate about your health condition. Use the following exercises to craft your story to share with the community.

(SG) This is a great exercise to have group members not only share their stories in words but also in pictures, music, art, etc.

There's power in sharing your personal story with others.

"If my mind can conceive it, and my heart can believe it, then I can achieve it."
—Muhammad Ali

➤ How are you helping spread awareness of the needs of your health condition's community?

There are "teachable moments" everywhere – at the store, at the elevator, restaurants, school, etc. Advocacy begins with sharing your personal story.

➤ Develop your story. Rehearse it.

➤ Tools for telling your story include: writing articles, editorials, elevator speeches, blogs, lectures, photographs, videos, etc.

➤ Find a platform and begin on a local basis to share your story.

➤ Tell your story in your community: to your friends/neighbors, church members, fellow civic group members, etc.

The more you share your story, the more empowered you will feel and become!

Let your voice be heard!

Use this space to create/develop your personal story!

Just Passing Through

Creative writing can be a powerful way to share your thoughts and feelings. Read the poem below and share your comments.

Don't stop sniffing the roses, you might just get a whiff!

There's so much to learn and discover something new.
The world is my classroom while I'm passing through.

Enjoy the stars and sun, snow and sand, and ocean of blue.
Preserve the joys of nature while you're passing through.

The planet was never ours to take; we didn't have a clue.
Cherish life for everything, while you're passing through.

The journey is as important as the destination; stop to see the view.
Savor what you can, because we're all just passing through.

➢ What do you get from this poem?

What Does a "Cure" Mean?

Use the questions below to discuss what a "cure" means to you.

Hope is powerful and with action, you get results.

➤ What does a cure mean to you?

　　○　Stopping your illness.

　　○　Reversing the effects of your illness.

➤ Until a cure is found, what can you do for yourself?

We Need a Cure

Answer the following questions to gauge your opinions about patience and obstacles.

Sharing knowledge and a positive perspective is contagious.

"Every individual makes a difference. We cannot live through a single day without making an impact on the world around us. And we all have free choice—what sort of difference do we want to make? Do we want to make the world around us a better place? Or not?"—Jane Goodall

➢ Discuss this quote.

In *A Soft Voice*, Karl discusses how Parkinson's disease does not have a cure and the effect the progression of the disease has on his and other lives. He shares his frustrations of not having a cure.

➢ Discuss Parkinson's/your health condition and patience.

   ❍ Are you patient?

➢ How much of your life is about waiting?

   ❍ Are you still active while you wait for a cure?

Challenges & Obstacles

We all face hurdles and obstacles in our life. The way we react to them is what matters!

➢ What do you see as your biggest hurdle to get over?

➢ Do you have a plan yet to overcome the hurdle?

➢ Do you have resources or know where to find the resources you need?

➤ Can someone you know search for you or have you looked for resources online to help you?

➤ Do you know someone who can help you?

 Do You Know?

Resource List in *A Soft Voice*

There is a resource section in the back of the original *A Soft Voice* book that has Parkinson's disease organization names, website addresses, short summaries, and more! Some support or communication groups have lending libraries that may have a copy of *A Soft Voice* that you can borrow. This book's publisher, RobbWorks, has a library program. Have your group facilitator or leader, hosting organization or local library contact RobbWorks at asoftvoice@robbworks.com for copies of the *A Soft Voice in a Noisy World* paperback.

A Surge of Urgency for Treatments and Cures

Treatments and cures for health conditions can take a long time for development. Consider the following sentences and how you feel about waiting for these discoveries.

These questions may be an opportunity to have discussions within the group about clinical trial participation and patient advocacy within the community.

Capturing time is like clutching an ice cube in August.

➢ Are you frustrated by the lack of progress of scientific breakthroughs for your health condition?

➢ Do you feel a sense of urgency to move forward?

  ○ Better drugs?

  ○ Therapies?

➢ What are you willing to do to move things ahead?

➢ What solutions do you propose to fight for and rally towards?

➢ Are you going to become active in your health condition's community?

Put some ideas on paper or on your computer.

➢ Where do you see yourself making a difference?

Getting involved and assisting others helps yourself. Find and fill a need in your area.

Offer others hope!

Lessons Learned from My Health Condition

There are insights and epiphanies that you have logged on your journey with your health condition. Take the time to write your lessons down to share with others. Try to dig deep and recall what lessons you have learned from your health condition. Your lessons may be humorous, serious, or both.

 **For those leading support, communication, exercise or meet up groups – use this exercise for 2 or 3 meetings for discussion.**

In *A Soft Voice,* there is an extensive list of insights/lessons learned from living with Parkinson's disease. Here are just a small sample of those insights/lessons:

➤ You have a choice how you treat yourself and others. Starting the day with a smile and a positive perspective brightens your day and those you encounter.

➤ Tell the people in your life how much they mean to you. Do something unexpected, like coming home from work early to play with your kids, taking your spouse out for lunch, or doing something as simple as writing a love poem and offering a hug.

➤ Laugh as much as you can.

➤ Never let illness defeat you. Your will and drive to heal, can and will, overcome PD. Each day brings hope for improvement. Your thoughts are capable of assisting your body to improve from its current state. Do your best to take care of yourself and preserve your health.

➤ Be kind to yourself as you face this daunting challenge. Living and battling illness takes grit, perseverance, patience, determination, focus, and a sense of humor.

➤ There is a place for conventional medicine and complementary medicine. You must uncover what works for you. Only through exploration, personal growth, education, and discovery can you proceed with healing. Understand your illness as fully as you can so that you may make the wisest decisions to overcome your ailment.

FINAL INSIGHTS

➤ Say thank you to your caregiver, carepartner, family, friends, medical team, and anyone else that helps you. It is important that you acknowledge their contributions to your life and health.

➤ Identify five of your own insights to share with others!

_____

_____

_____

_____

_____

➤ Pick two or three and share with the group or family/friends.

Conclusion

You may find benefit in doing the exercises and questions more than once. Try making some of these a part of your day.

It is our sincere hope that this workbook helps you and those around you with your experiences in living well with a health condition.

Thank you for taking time to do these exercises! Continue to learn, inspire, and grow!

All our best,
Angela & Karl

Insight Worksheets

Finish these statements to help you find greater insight into living well with your health condition. These questions are mostly for individuals but can be used in a group.

1. I need to _____.

2. I would like to improve _____.

3. My biggest issue right now is _____.

4. I really want to change my _____.

5. My attitude is _____ and people respond _____ to it.

6. I'm having trouble with _____.

7. I'm doing _____ for my Parkinson's/my health condition.

8. My biggest fear about Parkinson's/my health condition is_____.

9. Anxiety and stress worsened my health condition symptoms and increased my use of _____ to counteract it.

10. Parkinson's/my health condition has cost me _____.

11. I have lost _____ because of Parkinson's/my health condition.

12. I have regained _____.

13. I'm confident that _____.

14. Parkinson's/my health condition has taught me _____.

15. I plan for the future and _____.

16. My doctor _____.

17. My spouse _____.

18. My friends _____.

19. I now understand _____.

20. I don't understand _____.

21. I have improved my _____.

22. I'm working hard on _____.

23. _____ is going really well.

24. _____ has gotten much harder for me.

25. I find I need to educate _____.

26. People don't understand _____.

27. I feel lonely/not alone because _____.

28. I wish_____.

29. Living with Parkinson's/my health condition takes _____.

30. Finding balance with Parkinson's/my health condition requires
    _____.

31. I do _____ to stay grounded and focused.

32. I discovered great benefit from _____.

33. I need to change _____ in my life.

34. My biggest triggers and stressors in my life are _____.

35. I'm sensitive about _____.

36. I get stressed at _____.

37. I really enjoy _____.

38. I want to learn more on _____ .

39. I know that there's more to do for myself and the first thing to investigate is
_____ .

40. I need a plan, and part of the plan involves _____ .

41. My doctor doesn't _____   _____ .

42. Just because I have Parkinson's/my health condition doesn't mean
_____ .

43. I still dream of _____ .

44. A cure means _____ .

45. The lesson in having Parkinson's/my health condition is _____ .

46. Doing all you can for yourself and your illness means _____ .

47. My perspective about living with Parkinson's/my health condition is
_____ .

48. Parkinson's/my health condition is a challenge that _____ .

49. Tools to take on Parkinson's/my health condition are _____ .

50. The best place to get information on Parkinson's/my health condition is _____.

51. My biggest frustration is _____.

52. I want to understand _____.

53. My mind, body, and spirit work _____ together and could probably work even better together.

54. My breathing is _____.

55. I take _____ care of myself.

56. There is more that I could be doing for myself like, _____.

57. I need to be more mindful about _____.

58. I am a _____ listener and need to _____ to improve my communication skills.

Support Group Rules

The following are the rules that we devised for the support group we founded. Feel free to use them in your group/new group or modify them based on feedback from your group.

1. What is said in the group, stays in the group. Trust is the foundation of a group's success. Privacy and respect go hand in hand.

2. As a support group member you will find that your role may shift over time. At first, become acclimated to the group and as you get more secure and at ease you will become more involved and attuned to the whole process.

3. Be a good listener: Part of being a good support group member involves you being present, open, and listening to the other members. Really hearing what is said in the group and offering feedback adds to group discussion.

4. Share knowledge: We all have insight and perspective to offer. Your opinion may be of great help to someone who hasn't had your experience. You have a lot to offer. Brighten someone's day (and your own) with an unexpected compliment!

5. Don't just come: You are not obligated to do anything as a member, but if you want your group to flourish and thrive, you might help the leader in finding interesting speakers, topics, building interesting conversation, stepping up to help to bringing in new members, and making them feel welcomed.

6. Complacency: Groups fail because of complacency! If you expect your group to grow and bring in new members, don't rely totally on your leaders. Everyone needs to be involved in the group to make it the best that it can be.

7. The more you give, the more you get! A good member knows when to listen and when to offer their own expertise. Saying too much can weigh on your group or create domination and tie up the interactive flow of the group. Saying too little may make you appear unengaged or aloof.

8. Less tech, more you! If you have to have your cell phone with you, make sure it is on mute. This is a time to share with people and to be present. Give them the attention, focus, and energy that they deserve.

9. Stand up! If you see injustice or an error that needs rectifying, you may want to pull aside the support group leader and share with him or her. If it can wait, tell them after the meeting. Try to avoid conflict or added tension. If the error needs immediate attention, it is probably best to clarify it then and there.

10. Don't dominate time! Share it. Members should leave the group feeling educated, heard, and fulfilled!

Support Group Discussion Starter Worksheet

For groups – **Use these statements and questions as discussion starters for your meetings.**

For individuals – **If you are working solo, you may find these exercises are helpful in doing your own self-discovery.**

1. My biggest concern today is _____.

2. I'm going to start _____.

3. I want to change my _____ but I'm not sure how. Any ideas?

4. Let's talk about _____.

(SG) 5. Can someone tell me _____?

(SG) 6. Is there a drug to help _____?

(SG) 7. Is anyone here doing a therapy that has helped _____?

(SG) 8. Who here knows _____?

9. Where can I get help on _____?

10. What can I do to help my _____?

11. My doctor _____.

12. My medications make me _____.

13. How can I improve my _____?

14. My sleep is _____.

15. Something I do that helps my _____ is _____.

16. What I find that's been most helpful is _____.

17. I need more information on _____.

(SG) 18. For the next meetings, I suggest that we _____.

(SG) 19. _____ might be a good idea/topic for the next meeting.

(SG) 20. We should get a speaker on _____ for a future meeting.

(SG) **Discussion Exercise**

Take five minutes to write five questions about your health condition to address with the group.

After five minutes, ask the group to share their questions and spend the remainder of the meeting addressing the questions.

The Honesty Exercise

It is often remarked that the best exercise is the one you'll do. The key to finding what you like is exposing yourself to what you haven't tried yet. Be sure to try one new therapy or exercise at a time so you know which one is working for you.

➤ What are you willing to try?

➤ Is there a therapy that you may want to try, again?

➤ Are you committed to trying and staying with a certain therapy?

➤ Are you dedicated to helping yourself?

  Not Very dedicated   1   2   3   4   5   Very dedicated

➤ Do you care what others think?

  I care a little   1   2   3   4   5   I care a lot

Humor Exercise/Worksheet

Let's laugh! Think of what brings you to laughter.

What makes you laugh or smile?

_____

_____

Make a List:

Funny Movies?

Funny Television?

Funny Books? Comics?

Funny Audio?

When was the last time you laughed?

_____

What made you laugh?

_____

List three movies, three comics, three comedians who make you laugh.

_____

_____

Share a funny story or memory with the group, spouse, or someone you know!

The Pledge of the Ill

I accept my illness, but it does not define me. I am so much more, even if my illness masks or prohibits others from seeing who I am. Though I am different, I reserve the right to receive patience, respect, and some level of understanding from those I encounter in my everyday life.

I acknowledge that I have a duty to myself to explore all potential modes of healing whether they are conventional or out of the mainstream. I am worthy of being cared for by medical practitioners who treat me with respect and are willing to listen to me. I deserve to be recognized by my physician or other healthcare provider as a person with a life, not just as someone with a medical problem and a chart. My physician owes me the understanding to speak with me as an equal and as a human being, making my way through life as best as I possibly can.

I am willing to make changes, adjustments, and even sacrifices of monumental proportion if these therapies will assist in my betterment and the betterment of the lives of those around me. I am a representative of all those others, before and yet to follow me, who are afflicted with my very same illness. I will do all that I can for myself and those who are similarly afflicted.

I am on a journey to health and healing. I will share my insights and take time to educate all who will listen to me about my disease. The world needs more compassion, and only through education and understanding can we gain true compassion. I don't need, want, or desire any kind of sympathy, because sympathy is far too close to pity. All I ask for is assistance in moving along my path to achieve, learn, teach, grow, and inspire.

Moving Forward Worksheet

Complete these sentences and answer the questions based on how you feel at the time.

I hope to/want to/will try:

1. _____

2. _____

3. _____

4. _____

I am hesitant to try _____ because _____.

How can I get over this hurdle? _____
_____

Fear, anger, stress, and insecurity are major triggers to making Parkinson's/your health condition symptoms worse.

What are you going to do for yourself?_____
_____

How will you continue to improve or work to improve your health?_____
_____

No one knows their future, but…

Where do you hope to be in 6 months?

_____

Where do you hope to be in a year?

_____

Where do you hope to be in 3 years?

_____

Where do you hope to be in 5 years?

_____

Where do you hope to be in 10 years?

_____

What do you do to keep in balance? _____

_____

Exploring My Self-Care Worksheet

Answer the questions and complete the sentences as best you can. Your answers may change often.

➤ What can I do to help myself today? _____

➤ What tool would best help me? _____

➤ What new tool would I like to try? _____

➤ What can I give myself? _____

➤ What one change can I implement today to provide myself more self-care?

_____

_____

➤ I owe myself _____

➤ I take care of myself by _____

Here's some examples to stimulate your own answers about self care.

Ideas	Quiet Time	Fun
Travel	Dance	Exercise
Laughter	A movie night	To Sing
To Yell	To get out of my head	A hot bath
Play with my dog	To emote	

Perspective Exercise

Circle a word(s) that apply to you.

I am _____!

Strong	Funny	Smart	Kind
Creative	Caring	Thoughtful	Understanding
Mindful	Needed	Peaceful	Compassionate
Capable	Forgiving	Friendly	Making a Contribution
Careful	Worthy	Loving	Passionate

I know I can _____!

laugh more	live well	try more	expand my horizons
appreciate more	do more	smile more	savor more
learn more	love more	teach others	take better care of myself
say thank you more	make life better	honor myself	give more
honor my loved ones	work harder	appreciate myself	show more appreciation

I am a strong individual and I know I'm capable of _____!

loving more	taking on a challenge	showing compassion	more understanding
being thankful	showing who I am	being a better partner	greater appreciation
forgiveness	being a better listener	helping myself	honoring myself
honoring others	being a better friend	learning more	achieving a new goal
starting something new	setting a new goal	caring more	being involved

Personal Observations:

Try using your own words:

_____

_____

_____

_____

_____

_____

_____

_____

Hoping/Wishing/Working Worksheet

Set some goals for the short and long term!

Balance	Goals	
	Short Term	Long Term
Emotional		
Intellectual		
Spiritual		
Physical		
Network		
Health		
Overall Knowledge		
Relationships		
Medical		
Financial		

Fear Worksheet

Gain a better understanding of fear through this exercise:

1. What scares you the most?

2. How do you deal with fear?

3. Does fear hold you back?

4. What do you need to do to move forward?

Discuss what you think it might take to overcome your fears!

Self-Discovery Exercise

Complete the following sentences to gain more insight about what you are feeling.

I don't enjoy _____ nearly as much as
I used to, since _____ .

Finding balance with my health condition requires _____ _____
_____ .

My health condition is a challenge that _____
_____ .

I know I need _____

The best place to get information on my health condition is _____
_____ .

I am not my illness. I am _____ .

Maybe, if I don't fight my health condition but focus on the symptom at hand, I can
_____ .

I am willing to try _____ to get better.

My dedication to getting better requires _____ .

I'll never _____ .

APPENDIX XII

I will always _____.

I am sure that _____.

Support groups are _____.

I would like to share _____.

I need more information on _____.

I must work on _____ to see improvement.

Change is not always easy, but it is _____.

I would explain my health condition as a _____
_____.

About the Authors

Angela Robb is a wife and carepartner for her husband, Karl. Angela speaks and writes about dealing with caregiver/carepartner issues. In 2015, she was honored as a White House Champion of Change in Parkinson's Disease. She has spoken at the 3rd World Parkinson Congress (Montréal), Davis Phinney Foundation Victory Summit® (*Richmond & Charlotte*), Partners in Parkinson's DC, NPF Young Onset Parkinson Network conferences, and various regional PD conferences. She has written on the topic of caregiver self-care for the Davis Phinney Foundation's *Every Victory Counts®* manual. She is a board member of the Parkinson Voice Project.

Professionally, she is a certified Reiki Master/instructor and co-owner and creative director for RobbWorks. She has a B.A. in Political Science/Public Policy from West Virginia University. You can contact her at angela@givereiki.com or @angelarobbva on Twitter.

Karl Robb has had Parkinson's disease for over twenty-five years. With symptoms since he was seventeen years old, Karl was diagnosed at the age of twenty-three. Now 50, he is a Parkinson's advocate, entrepreneur, inventor, author, blogger, lecturer, photographer, and a certified Reiki Master.

Karl earned a bachelor's degree in English from the University of North Carolina at Chapel Hill. His work on Parkinson's issues has been featured by *The New York Post,* BBC Radio, the CBS News, and NHK World Television, as well as several Washington, D.C., television stations.

Karl is a board member of the Parkinson Voice Project.

To contact Karl, email him at karl@asoftvoice.com.

Stay in touch with Karl at his website: www.ASoftVoice.com

Twitter: https://www.twitter.com/asoftvoicePD

Facebook: http://www.facebook.com/pages/A-Soft-Voice-in-a-Noisy-World-by-Karl-Robb/156649751148007

Watch for our upcoming book: *Words of Hope*

More books are coming soon… stay in touch through our website,
www.ASoftVoice.com

Made in the USA
Columbia, SC
09 August 2019